SIGHT WORDS

Written by **Shannon Keeley**

Illustrated by **Maru Jara**

FlashKids

A Division of Barnes & Noble Publishing

This book belongs to

_____

Spark Educational Publishing
A Division of Barnes & Noble Publishing
120 Fifth Avenue
New York, NY 10011

ISBN 1-4114-0011-9

Please submit changes or report errors to www.sparknotes.com/errors

Printed and bound in China

For more information, please visit www.flashkidsbooks.com

Word Find

The word **the** is hidden two times in each line.
Find the words and circle them.

e h t h e e t h t h e t

t e h e t h e e h t h e

and

Practice writing the word **and**. Say the word aloud.

and

Write the word to complete the sentence.

Put on your coat ___ ___ ___ hat.

Rhyme Time

Circle the pictures that rhyme with **and**.

Underline the letters **a-n-d** in each rhyming word.

man

hand

sand

mad

Practice writing the word **a**. Say the word aloud.

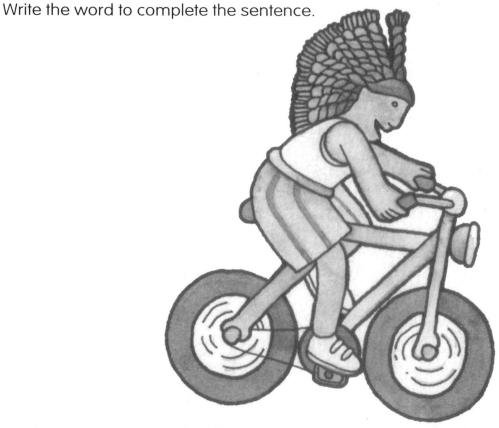

Write the word to complete the sentence.

I have ___ bike.

Color the Pictures

Color the balloons that have the word **a**.

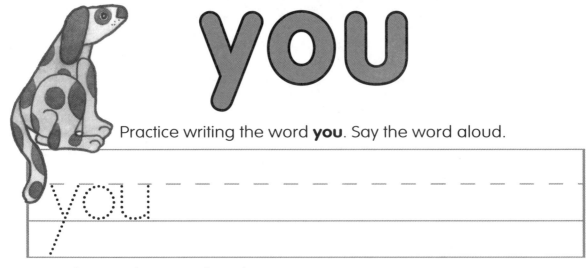

YOU

Practice writing the word **you**. Say the word aloud.

you

Write the word to complete the sentence.

He likes ___ ___ ___ .

Maze

Help the turtle solve the maze. Connect the letters to make **you**.

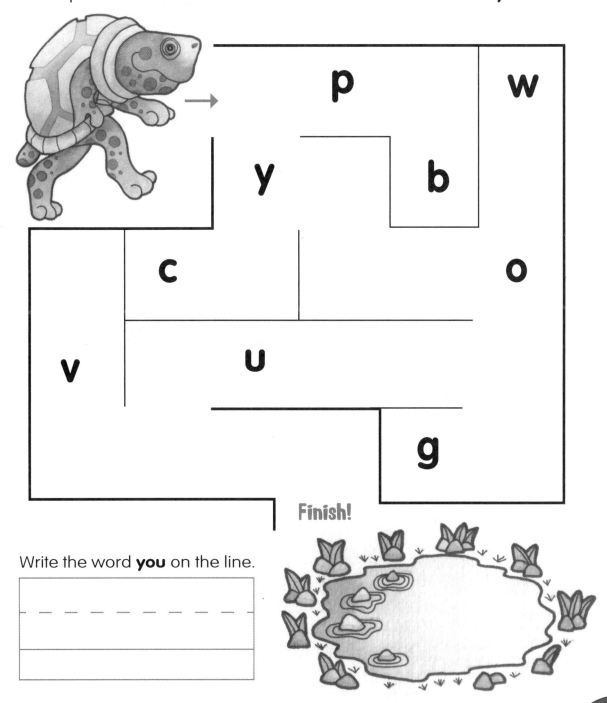

Write the word **you** on the line.

of

Practice writing the word **of**. Say the word aloud.

of

Write the word to complete the sentence.

I have a box ___ ___ toys.

Tic Tac Toe

Circle the row that has the word **of** three times.

Then write **of** three times on the line below.

of	off	fo
of	of	of
ofo	of	if

Review: Word Search

Find the words in the word search.

Then write each word below.

the	and	a	you	of

y	t	o	u	a
o	h	e	f	d
u	a	n	d	n
t	h	e	h	y
o	d	u	o	e

Review: Story Time

Write the correct word to complete each sentence in the story.

the   and   a   you   of

Dear Friend,

I have something

for ___ ___ ___. It's ___ gift.

It's sweet ___ ___ ___

chewy. What is

___ ___ ___ gift?

A box ___ ___ cookies!

he

Practice writing the word **he**. Say the word aloud.

Write the word to complete the sentence.

Look, ___ ___ is my brother.

Word Find

The word **he** is hidden two times in each line.

Find the words and circle them.

e h e e h h e h t h c e

h e h h h a h o h e h

it

Practice writing the word **it**. Say the word aloud.

Write the word to complete the sentence.

What is __ __ ?

Rhyme Time

Circle the pictures that rhyme with **it**.
Underline the letters **i-t** in each word.

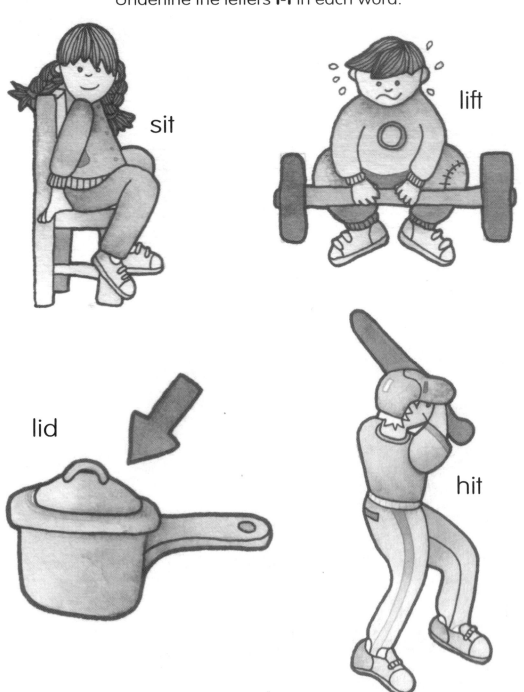

sit

lift

lid

hit

I

Practice writing the word **I**. Say the word aloud.

I

Write the word to complete the sentence.

____ **like ice cream.**

Color the Pictures

Color the leaves that have the word **I**.

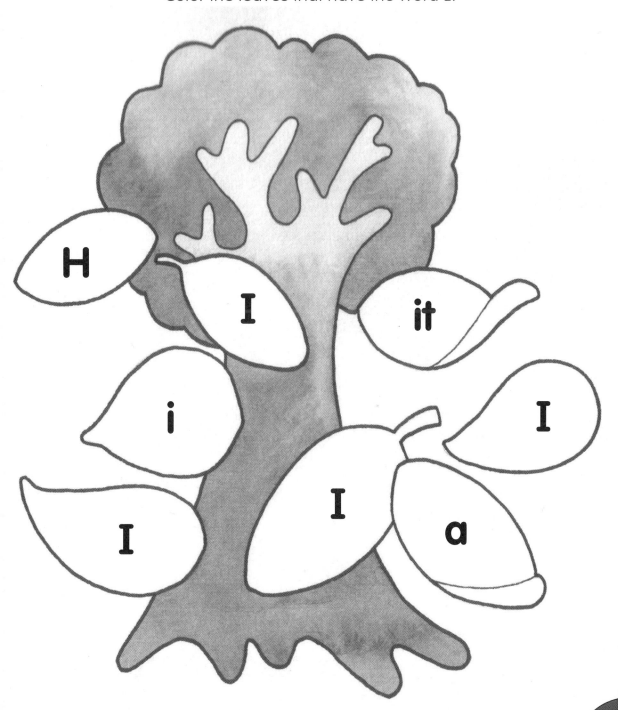

had

Practice writing the word **had**. Say the word aloud.

had

Write the word to complete the sentence.

I ___ ___ ___ a good time.

Maze

Help the bunny solve the maze. Connect the letters to make **had**.

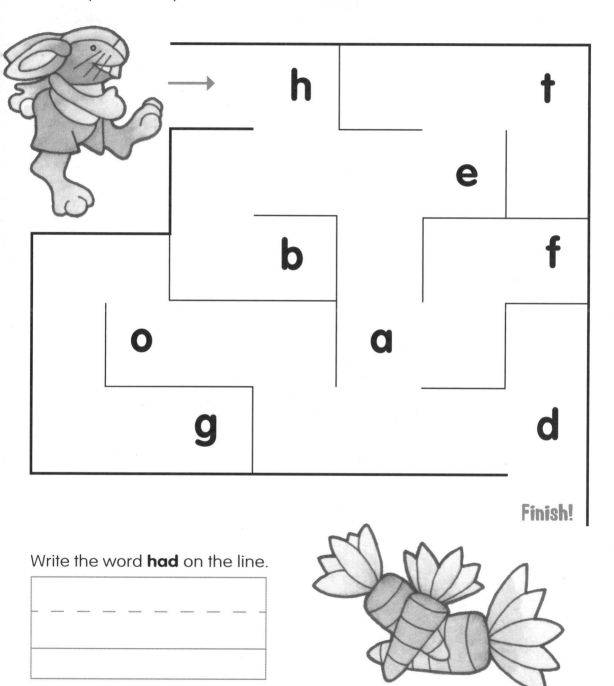

h   t

e

b   f

o   a

g   d

Finish!

Write the word **had** on the line.

we

Practice writing the word **we**. Say the word aloud.

we

Write the word to complete the sentence.

Today ___ ___ played.

Tic Tac Toe

Circle the row that has the word **we** three times.

Then write **we** three times on the line below.

we	me	we
ew	we	we
we	we	wee

Review: Word Search

Find the words in the word search. Then write each word below.

he	it	I	had	we

i	d	h	a	i
h	w	a	w	t
w	o	d	h	e
I	u	a	i	a
d	w	p	e	t

Review: Story Time

Write the correct word to complete each sentence in the story.

| he | it | I | had | we |

___ went to my brother's birthday party.

Yesterday, ___ ___ turned five years old,

and ___ ___ gave him a big cake. He

loved ___ ___ ! We ___ ___ ___ so much fun.

was

Practice writing the word **was**. Say the word aloud.

was

Write the word to complete the sentence.

The cookie ___ ___ ___ good.

Word Find

The word **was** is hidden two times in each line.

Find the words and circle them.

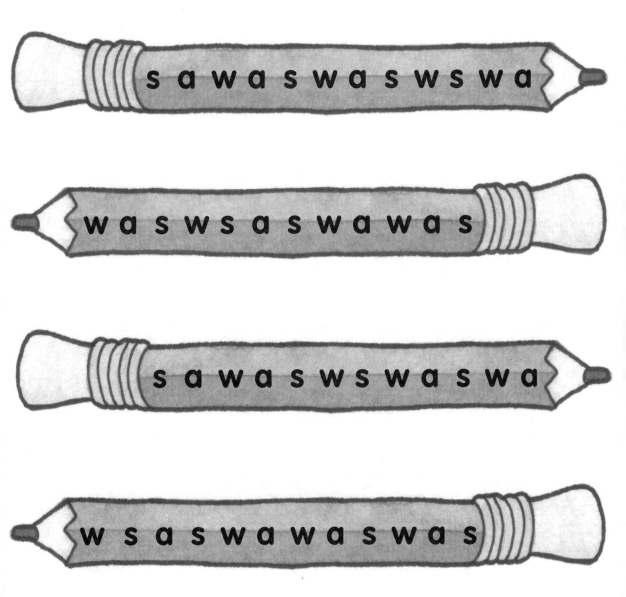

s a w a s w a s w s w a

w a s w a s w a w a s

s a w a s w s w a s w a

w s a s w a w a s w a s

at

Practice writing the word **at**. Say the word aloud.

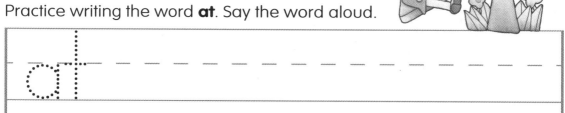

Write the word to complete the sentence.

I am ___ ___ the park.

Rhyme Time

Circle the pictures that rhyme with **at**.

Underline the letters **a-t** in each rhyming word.

cat

hat

dad

ant

she

Practice writing the word **she**. Say the word aloud.

she

Write the word to complete the sentence.

Where does _____ _____ _____ live?

Color the Pictures

Color the gumballs that have the word **she**.

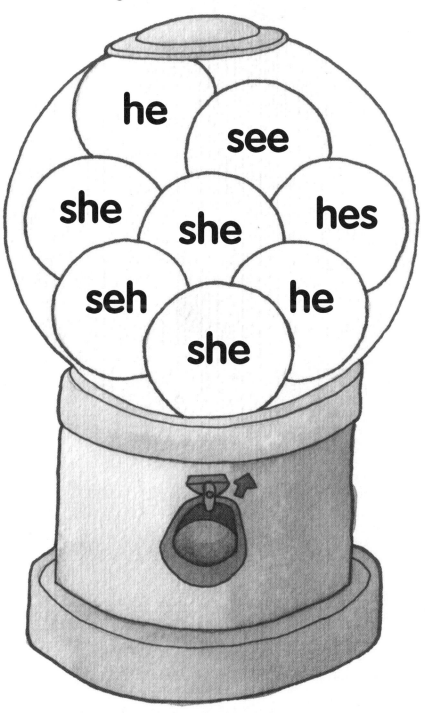

but

Practice writing the word **but**. Say the word aloud.

but

Write the word to complete the sentence.

I wanted to play outside, ___ ___ ___ it rained.

Maze

Help the pup solve the maze. Connect the letters to make **but**.

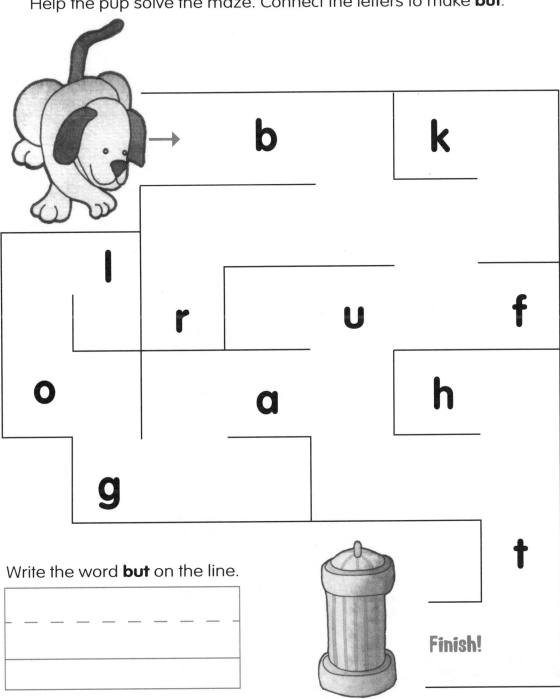

Write the word **but** on the line.

on

Practice writing the word **on**. Say the word aloud.

on

Write the word to complete the sentence.

Put them __ __ the table.

Tic Tac Toe

Circle the row that has the word **on** three times.

Then write **on** three times on the lines below.

no	on	on
one	on	of
on	an	on

Review: Word Search

Find the words in the word search. Then write each word below.

was	at	she	but	on

b u w a t

a w s h u

o a s o t

n s h e o

w b u t b

Review: Story Time

Write the correct word to complete each sentence in the story.

was	she	on	at	but

It ____ ____ ____ a sunny day.

Anna and I were ____ ____ the park.

Anna said ____ ____ ____ wanted to swing,

____ ____ ____ the swings were broken.

So we played ____ ____ the slide.

to

Practice writing the word **to**. Say the word aloud.

to

Write the word to complete the sentence.

Let's go ___ ___ school.

Word Find

The word **to** is hidden two times in each line.
Find the words and circle them.

t t o o t o a t t f o t

o o t o o t t f t o o t

all

Practice writing the word **all**. Say the word aloud.

all

Write the word to complete the sentence.

Pick up ___ ___ ___ the candy.

Rhyme Time

Circle the pictures that rhyme with **all**.

Underline the letters **a-l-l** in each rhyming word.

nail

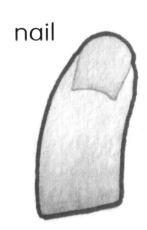

pal

fall

ball

for

Practice writing the word **for**. Say the word aloud.

for — — — — — — — — — —

Write the word to complete the sentence.

This gift is ___ ___ ___ you.

Color the Pictures

Color the rocks that have the word **for**.

said

Practice writing the word **said**. Say the word aloud.

said

Write the word to complete the sentence.

Mom ___ ___ ___ ___ to wear a coat.

Maze

Help the cat solve the maze. Connect the letters to make **said**.

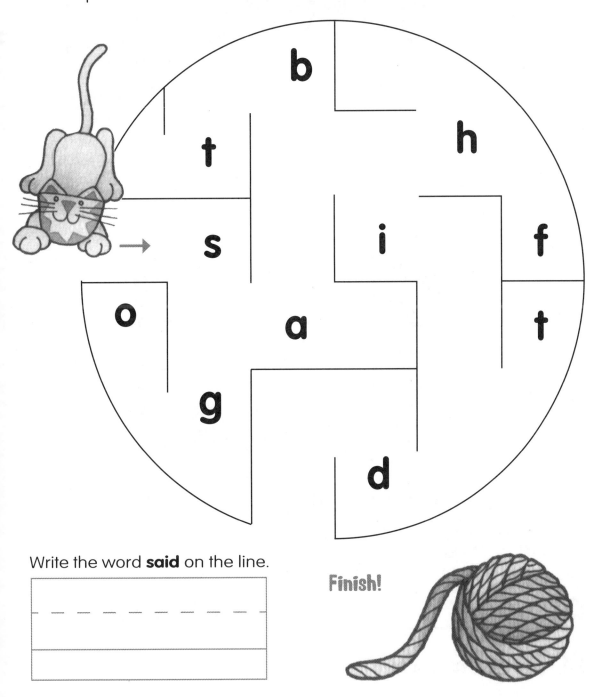

Write the word **said** on the line.

Finish!

they

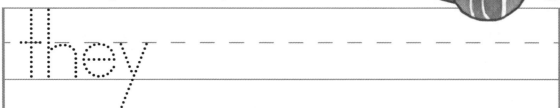

Practice writing the word **they**. Say the word aloud.

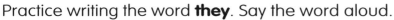

they

Write the word to complete the sentence.

Are ___ ___ ___ ___ on the same team?

Tic Tac Toe

Circle the row that has the word **they** three times.
Then write **they** three times on the lines below.

they	they	hey
they	the	they
they	thy	they

Review: Word Search

Find the words in the word search. Then write each word below.

to	all	for	said	they

y	t	f	o	a
s	t	h	a	l
f	o	r	e	l
s	a	d	t	y
l	s	a	i	d

Review: Story Time

Write the correct word to complete each sentence in the story.

to	all	for	said	they

My family had a party ___ ___ ___ me.

___ ___ ___ ___ got a big cake,

and we went ___ ___ the park.

"Happy Birthday," they ___ ___ ___ ___.

I blew out ___ ___ ___ the candles.

so

Practice writing the word **so**. Say the word aloud.

so

Write the word to complete the sentence.

The water was ___ ___ cold.

Word Find

The word **so** is hidden two times on each sign.

Find the words and circle them.

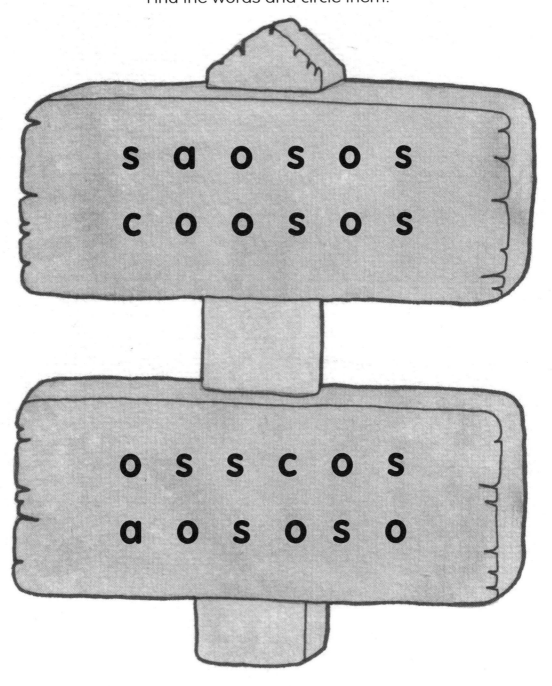

s a o s o s

c o o s o s

o s s c o s

a o s o s o

in

Practice writing the word **in**. Say the word aloud.

in

Write the word to complete the sentence.

Get ___ ___ the tub!

Rhyme Time

Circle the pictures that rhyme with **in**.
Underline the letters **i-n** in the rhyming words.

on

fin

can

pin

with

Practice writing the word **with**. Say the word aloud.

with

Write the word to complete the sentence.

I played ___ ___ ___ ___ my friends.

Color the Pictures

Color the fish that have the word **with**.

there

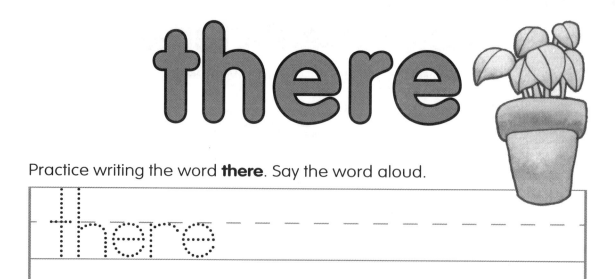

Practice writing the word **there**. Say the word aloud.

there

Write the word to complete the sentence.

My desk is over ___ ___ ___ ___ ___ .

Maze

Help the bug solve the maze. Connect the letters to make **there**.

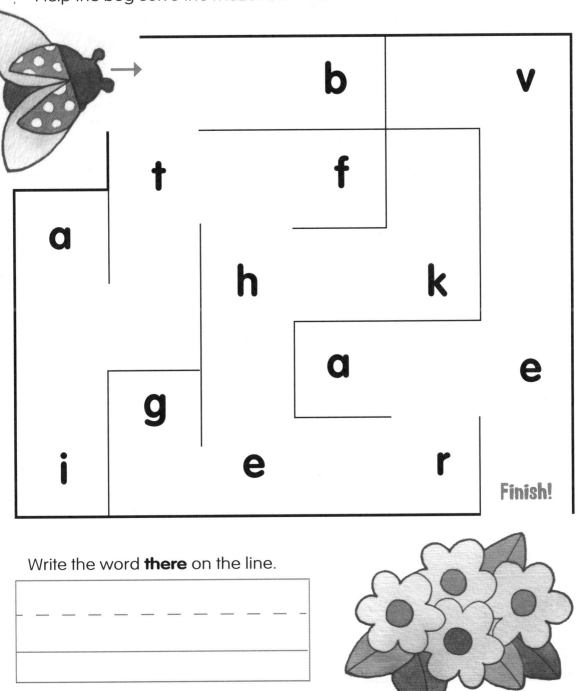

Write the word **there** on the line.

can

Practice writing the word **can**. Say the word aloud.

can

Write the word to complete the sentence.

I ___ ___ ___ help my mom.

Tic Tac Toe

Circle the row that has the word **can** three times.

Then write **can** three times on the lines below.

can	can	con
can't	cane	can
can	can	can

Review: Word Search

Find the words in the word search. Then write each word below.

so	in	with	there	can

t	h	w	i	t
a	n	i	o	h
c	o	t	i	e
r	a	h	n	r
s	o	n	r	e

Review: Story Time

Write the correct word to complete each sentence in the story.

so	in	with	there	can

"It's __ __ hot today," said Amy

"We __ __ __ go swimming," said Dad.

"Can my friend come __ __ __ __ us?"

asked Amy.

"Sure! Have her meet us __ __ __ __ __!"

"I can't wait to get __ __ the pool," said Amy.

Great job,

_____ .
(Name)

Now you know 25 sight words!